What helps you be a better writer?

Hopefully the more I write — and rewrite — it gets a little better.

What v ... ... for if you ...

I'd wish f whole no then I'd save it to the iCloud so it wouldn't vanish.

Your favourite way to spend the weekend is...

To have breakfast in bed and then a long read, to have a swim, to go to an art gallery, to do a bit of shopping, and then to have a meal with friends in the evening.

Which TV show would you love to star in?

If I were much younger I'd love to go on *Strictly Come Dancing*.

If you could have one special talent, what would it be?

I wish I could make things — I'd love to design my own Victorian doll house and make all the miniature furniture.

Which book have you read over and over again?

I Capture the Castle by Dodie Smith. I first read it when I was eleven, and I must have reread it at least ten times.

I Capture the Castle

Dodie Smith

D1587334

3

ALL ABOUT AMAZING ME!

Draw a doodle of yourself here!

Meet Me!

Real name __Hannah Stewart__

What I wish my name was! __Heather Stewart__

Age __11__

My JW Match!

Pick the JW character you're most like!

- ☐ Melissa
- ☐ Elsa
- ☐ Marty
- ☑ Jess
- ☐ Tina
- ☐ Katy

♥ My Favourites: ♥

Colour __Navy blue__

Book __The worry website__

Song __Valerie__

Animal __Puppy__

Film __No time to die__

- ☐ Spring
- ☐ Autumn
- ☐ Summer
- ☑ Winter

Be an Awesome Author!

You could be a brilliant best-selling author like Jacky! Turn over to get started with these writing tips and challenges!

Jacky's first big best-selling novel was *The Story of Tracy Beaker*. What will you call your best-selling book?

....

....

....

Take our reading and writing challenges!

KEEP READING,

How would you have written our stories?

OPAL PLUMSTEAD

'Do you believe in ghosts?' Olivia asked.

Use the first sentences from our books...

LOLA ROSE

Have you ever wondered what you'd do if you won the lottery?

... to start a totally new tale.

DIXIE DIAMOND

'I've got a surprise for you girls,' said Mum. 'We're moving.'

You can write whatever you like!

STELLA STEBBINS

I sat in the back of the car in my new t-shirt and my stiff new jeans and my pristine trainers and groaned.

The Rainbow of Writing

RED: The red dress made me feel daring and confident. I was brave and could take on any of those bullies!

ORANGE: The orange orange was very tasty and sweet.

YELLOW: I got a new fluffy yellow pen. It's very fun to write with.

GREEN: I saw a lovely green cardigan online.

BLUE: The azure blue pool was calm and serene. Swimming made me relax.

INDIGO: My indigo jumper makes me feel happy.

VIOLET: I'm going to violets party later!

DESCRIBE YOUR FEELINGS THROUGH COLOUR!

Mighty Mart is the superhero me! As Mart I can fly and vanquish pink!

I've given you two examples to get started.

KEEP WRITING!

IN THE NEWS!

> My story really got started with a newspaper headline!

DUSTBIN BABY!

College student Frankie Smith, 17, found a surprise waiting for him when he did his evening shift at The Pizza Place in the High Street yesterday. He heard a high-pitched wailing coming from the refuse bins at the back of the popular restaurant.

'I thought it was a cat,' said Frankie. 'I got the shock of my life when I took the dustbin lid off and saw the baby.'

The Daily News

DUSTBIN BABY!

Look for a newspaper headline that grabs your attention. Now write your own story based on the headline you choose.

> Ever wondered what happens to JW characters after the end of the story?

> Choose your fave book and write the next chapter of their tale.

WHAT HAPPENS NEXT?

- Think carefully about how the book ended and what you'd like to happen next.
- Perhaps a tragedy is turned into a triumph, or maybe the character finds fame and fortune!
- What about pairing up characters that appeared in different books?

It's all up to you, so pick up a pen and get started!

SUPER STORY

Who would you be if you were a superhero? Write your superhero story, describing your outfit and powers. How would you save the world? Who would be your nemesis?

SUPER GIRLY GIRL

Mortal enemy!

MY 2022 READING GOAL!

In 2022 I'm going to read one book

- ☐ EVERY WEEK
- ☐ EVERY TWO WEEKS
- ☑ EVERY MONTH

Signed: Hstewarts

MARIGOLD'S Zodiac Storyteller!

> Play my game to create a story that's written in the stars!

What to do:

- Turn to page 91 to find your Zodiac Story Cards. Cut them out and pop them in a bag.
- Roll a dice to make selections from sections A, B and C — story setting, character and story twist.
- Each time you play, pick out three random cards.
- Follow the cards to add extra plot twists to your story.
- Pick one card from the three you've chosen to reveal personality traits for your character.

Play again and again to get different outcomes!

A. Your story setting is...

1. Oops! You're locked in a shopping mall at night.

2. A theme park full of exciting rides and rollercoasters.

3. A really boring and tiresome school lesson.

4. You're staying in a super-creepy old hotel.

5. You have to work as a maid in a posh house.

6. An old-fashioned store selling all sorts of curious goods.

B. Your character is...

1. A Victorian orphan.
2. Tracy Beaker's long-lost twin.
3. A cheeky ten-year-old boy.
4. A spoiled rich girl.
5. A very shy and timid person.
6. A super-brainy know-it-all.

C. The twist is...

1. Things are not what they seem — everything has a magical power.
2. The story is set in the future.
3. Everything is made of candy and sweets!
4. You're in a comic world where everything is drawn, only you are real.
5. Everyone but you talks in rhyme.
6. The story is set in the past.

Turn to page 91 to find your Zodiac Story Cards!

THE ZODIAC STORY PLANNER

Fill in your outcomes to keep track of your story!

A. My story setting is
in a boring private school

B. My character is
outgoing and energy

C. The twist is
She acts different in school

My Zodiac Card plot twists are
1.
2.
3.

My character's personality traits are

Tip!
Think about how your character's strengths and weaknesses can affect your story. For example, if they're loud and outgoing, how will they behave during the boring school lesson?

9

Character Selector!

Stuck for character inspiration for your story? Not anymore!

PERSONALITY

What's your character like as a person? Find out here!

Add up all the numbers in your birthday until you're left with a single number. For example, you were born on October 12th, 2010:

12/10/2010

1+2+1+0+2+0+1+0 = 7

Your mystic number is 7!

1 Strange, imaginative and private
2 Suspicious, touchy and orderly
3 Bold, brave and tough
4 Wild, supportive and happy
5 Shy, modest and friendly
6 Disorganised, lively and easy-going
7 Independent, trusting and relaxed
8 Rebellious, sensitive and feisty
9 Confident, practical and calm

EYE COLOUR

Close your eyes and place your finger somewhere on this section — the butterfly your finger lands closest to reveals your character's eye colour!

Blue

Brown

Green

Hazel

Grey

Amber

HAIR

Do the same again in this section. Whichever duck your finger is closest to reveals your character's hair colour!

Blonde Pink Blue Red

Brown Black Green

FUN FACT!

Pick your favourite colour to find out something interesting about your character!

Your character is…

The eldest of 17 children!

Fluent in three languages!

Secretly scared of the dark!

A crime–fighting superhero by night!

Super–rich — but no one else knows!

Able to breathe under water!

100 years old!

A champion dog trainer!

GOODIE OR BADDIE?

Flip a coin to find out if your character is a goodie or a baddie!

HEADS – goodie
TAILS – baddie

BIRTH MONTH

JANUARY — Evelyn Montgomery
FEBRUARY — Melody Caldicot
MARCH — Suki Armstrong
APRIL — Rosetta Kingsley
MAY — Suzette Muircroft
JUNE — Bernadette Huntington
JULY — Tabitha Charlton
AUGUST — Veronica Smythson
SEPTEMBER — Jodie Dandridge
OCTOBER — Penelope Vanderbilt
NOVEMBER — Emilia Godfrey
DECEMBER — Marnie Caulfield

Sketch your character HERE!

MY CHARACTER!

Maybe your character has an angry expression or perhaps they're super-smiley!

What kind of clothes will your character wear?

Smart or casual, trendy or boring?

Is their hair neat and tidy or wild and wacky?

Are they big or small?

Why not stick on some paper or fabric scraps to bring your character to life?

Does your character have a pet? You could draw them, too!

You could add a speech bubble with a catchphrase they always say!

Name: Tabitha Charlton

Tracy's Tremendous

ACROSTIC
Pick a word and write it down the left side of your page. Each line of your poem should start with a word beginning with that letter!

HAIKU
A haiku is a three-line poem with a total of 17 syllables. The first and last line have 5, and the middle line 7!

DIAMANTE
This kind of poem is 7 lines long, and doesn't rhyme! It should be in a diamond shape, with the first and last lines shortest.

SHAPE
A shape poem should be written in the shape of the object it's describing. So if you're describing a ball, the poem should be a circle shape!

LIMERICK
A limerick is a funny five-line poem. Lines one and two should rhyme and lines three and four should rhyme with each other too. Line five should rhyme with one and two!

Poems!

Poems are the perfect way to test out lots of story ideas! Experiment with different forms for extra fun, and write your own!

Ahem... Try and beat this one!

TRACY

T – Tremendous Tracy, that's my name!
R – Really cool while playing the Dare Game!
A – Absolutely awesome, I'm such a hoot.
C – Completely gorgeous, as well to boot!
Y – You can't beat me, you're just a wannabe!

Write your own poem here!

It's just hayfever, I'm not crying!

The A-Z of Story Prompts!

Finding a new story to write is as easy as a, b, c!

A The **apples** from the orchard are so sweet. But the new owner has forbidden anyone from entering... they won't miss one little apple, right?

B "Your **best** friend's a dog? It can't even talk!" she said, scornfully. "Who says he can't?" I answered...

C You're alone in the forest on a **camping** trip. Suddenly, the hairs on the back of your neck stand up... someone is watching you...

D An antique **doll** comes to life as the clock strikes midnight. Is it a friend under an evil spell, or a deadly enemy waiting to strike?

E The train leaves the station at **eleven** every morning — you can't be late! Your mission is too important!

F "The first time I tried to be a **fashion** model was a complete disaster! The second time was even worse..."

G The old watch is **gold**. You can see an inscription: "To Gemma, from Jacob. Come find me". Surely it's a coincidence that you're called Gemma?

H Every day you walk by a little **house** with a blue door and a bright yellow fence. Who lives there?

I Your dad's an **inventor** and the house is filled with amazing contraptions and doodads. But his newest invention just might be the *best thing ever...*

J When you told that **joke** about the meanest, toughest girl in school, you never imagined that she'd burst into tears...

K There's a **knock** at the front door. You open it to discover the strangest creature you've ever seen. What does it look like — and what does it want?

L Oh, no — you're **lost** in a foreign city where you don't know the language! How do you communicate? How will you ever get back with no money?

M Your big sister becomes a **movie** star! How will her fame affect the rest of the family? Imagine if she took you to a big awards ceremony filled with stars!

N It wasn't until I removed the towel that I realised my hair had turned an alarming shade of **neon** green... and the dance was less than an hour away!

O The **Olympic** medal sat on my grandmother's dresser. "How did you ever get it?" I asked. "Well, that's a rather amazing story," she said...

P Write a mystery story about a talking **parrot**, a frozen pond and a stolen pearl necklace.

Q You find yourself on a **quest** to rid the kingdom of an evil tyrant. You're accompanied by a small pixie, a centaur and a talking mouse.

R Write about a girl with a magical talent for baking! What kind of spectacular dishes could she whip up in her spell-binding **restaurant**?

S Write about a secret school for the children of **superheroes** ... and spies! Do students have any special powers of their own? What about the teachers?

T **Trick-or-treat**! You're feeling super-brave and ignore the warnings not to knock on old Mrs Mayfair's door. People say she's a witch...

U The Beckeridge Academy **uniform** was forest green with silver trim — how posh. I gulped. Perhaps going to boarding school was a terrible mistake...

V Ordinary girl by day, **vampire** hunter by night? Who knew living a double life could be so exhausting — especially when someone discovers your secret!

W The old **window** is caked with dirt. You use your sleeve to clean it off and peer through. You were right! The thieves are using it as a hideout!

X The doctor starts up the **X-ray** machine. There's a blinding flash and a bang! When you open your eyes, you're not in the hospital any more...

Y **Yesterday** was Friday — but today is Friday too! You're stuck in a time-loop and have to live the same day over and over. How will you break the loop?

Z Your best friend is having a birthday sleepover at the local **zoo**! Brilliant! At least it was until the tiger managed to escape its enclosure... *gulp*!

IMAGINE IF...
You Were A Magazine Editor!

Imagine if you had the chance to edit JW Mag — what would you do?

7.30am
Get up and have a hot drink, you've a long day ahead!

9am
Get into the office and start brainstorming ideas!

1pm
Time for some lunch!

2pm
Now it's time to bake that rainbow cake for the magazine! Remember, you have to take pictures of each step!

11am
Meet Jacky and show her the latest pages in the magazine!

4pm
You have to edit everyone's work... There can't be a single spelling mistake! Now you know how Jacky feels when she has to proof-read all of her books — phew!

6pm
Time to call it quits after a looong day and have a lovely soak in the tub... Maybe you'll be struck with inspiration, just like Jacky when she named Tracy Beaker!

Did you know that Jacky used to be a magazine journalist?

16

Story Scenario!

Imagine one of these scenarios. Write a one-page story about how you'd handle it!

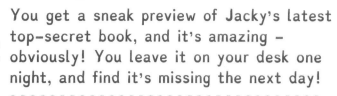

You have two hours until deadline, when suddenly, your computer crashes and your entire magazine is lost!

You find out that one of your journalists is selling your top editing secrets to another magazine!

You get a sneak preview of Jacky's latest top-secret book, and it's amazing – obviously! You leave it on your desk one night, and find it's missing the next day!

You are up for a top magazine award, but when you go to leave your office, you realise that you are locked in!

Now it's time to design your very first front cover!

The Official **Jacqueline Wilson** Mag

Who would your JW cover star be?

Pick a yummy treat to bake!

Draw your cover star here!

What is Jacky's new book about?

What JW book are you reviewing?

Why not write some of the stories you feature on the cover?

My Writing Secrets!

Take a trip through time with me!

I've written quite a few books set in the past, from the Victorian era in *Hetty Feather* to the Edwardian age in *Opal Plumstead*. I did all sorts of research before I put pen to paper because I wanted to make sure I got every detail just right. It would have been so much easier — and much more fun! — if I could've stepped back in time to see for myself!

Let's imagine that we have our very own time machine! It can visit any point in time from the very beginning of the world to present day, at the touch of a button.

I think it would be fun to choose one of my JW characters, pluck them from their current era, and send them off to another time altogether! It would certainly make for a very interesting story, don't you think?

Pick one girl!

Edwardian ☐

Victorian ☐

50s ☐

60s ☐ *Me as a teen!*

✔ Present day!

Think about your chosen character, what she likes to wear, how she talks, where she lives, whether she's poor or rich and what kind of school she goes to. What are her friends and family like? Jot down some notes here:

....
....
....
....
....
....
....

Time Machine!

Now for the really fun part! Use the time machine below to send your character back, or forward, in time! Simply pick an era from the dial, or spin a pencil to choose a period of time at random.

Before you write the rest of your story, have a think about how your character will react to this new, unfamiliar era. Here are some suggestions to get your imagination in gear!

EGYPTIAN

VICTORIAN

MEDIEVAL

TODAY

WORLD WAR II

STONE AGE

FUTURE

EDWARDIAN

How has fashion changed?

How do people communicate?

Where will your character live and work in this new era?

Will your character embrace this new way of life, or will they hate it?

Maybe robots (or dinosaurs!) are roaming the earth!

What are the schools like? There may not even be any!

Perhaps people now live on another planet!

Your character might meet up with a relative of theirs!

Do people have different beliefs or customs?

Use lots of description in your story to bring your setting, characters and plot twists to life!

My Writing Tips!

I solve your writing dilemmas!

A. Oh, I know the feeling. When I was a child I never finished stories either. If you get stuck, I'd put the story away, try to forget about it for a little while, and then read it through. You might get inspired all over again.

Q. I can't think up good ideas for stories!

A. Sometimes you can try almost too hard. Don't stress about it. Just keep your eyes and ears open. You might see someone unusual going down the street, see something surprising on television, overhear an interesting conversation... you can get ideas in so many different ways.

My writing dilemma is...

....

....

....

To solve it, I'm going to...

....

....

....

Q. I'd like to write a story set in the past, but I'm not sure how to get all the details just right...

A. It's important to read a history book or two that covers your intended history period, just so you don't make any obvious mistakes — but basically it's all a matter of trying to imagine what it was like to live long ago.

BECOME A CRAFT QUEEN

MAKE-UP GIFTS

Show off your crafting skills to create marvellous makes and darling DIYs!

Stick a picture of something you've made here!

MARVELLOUS MEMORY BOX!

What's inside this brilliant book? Surprise and amaze your friends with its hidden treasure!

YOU'LL NEED:
- Cereal box
- White card
- Red and yellow paint
- Gold marker
- Black pen
- Velcro sticky dots
- Ruler
- Scissors
- Double-sided tape

THE MEMOIRS OF HETTY FEATHER

What will you store inside your secret box?
- Jewellery
- Mementos
- Stationery
- Diary

Cut around the dotted line and use this to decorate your journal!

1 Measure the amount of card you'll need to cover your cereal box — the front, back and side for the spine. Leave about 1.5 cm all around the box to give the impression of a hardback book and cut out.

2 Tape the open end of your box closed. Use a pair of scissors to carefully cut along three edges at the front of the box, leaving the spine side still attached.

3 Cover the box with double-sided sticky tape or glue. Carefully stick the card in place, using your pencil marks as guides.

4 Cut out two triangles of card. Fold over two edges and glue inside your box corners, like this. Add Velcro sticky dots to keep your cover closed!

5 Cover your workstation with old newspaper, then paint your book cover red — make sure you get the inside edges, too! Leave to dry.

WHY NOT?
Become the author of your own book and make up your own title! Or you could re-create your favourite JW cover, instead!

6 Measure the short sides of your cereal box and cut out white card to fit each one. Draw lines with black marker and a ruler to make pages. Stick in place.

7 Use your gold pen to decorate the book cover and spine. Place all your treasures inside the box and pop it on your shelf — no one will know what's inside!

Make TEENY TINY THINGS!

Make super-cute stuff! Awww!

Teeny Bouquet!

YOU'LL NEED:
- ✓ Green craft sticks (we trimmed the excess fuzz off ours!)
- ✓ Tissue paper
- ✓ Glue
- ✓ Cellophane
- ✓ Scissors
- ✓ Sticky tape

1 Make mini flowers by gluing balls of tissue paper to craft sticks. Leave to dry.

2 Cut a square of tissue paper and a square of cellophane and lay the cellophane on top of the tissue paper. Fold in half, twisting slightly, and place the flowers on top.

3 Fold the left side of the bouquet over the flowers...

4 ...Then the right side over the left, securing with a tiny bit of sticky tape — done!

Tiny Box!

YOU'LL NEED:

- ✓ Paper
- ✓ Card
- ✓ Double-sided sticky tape
- ✓ Sweets
- ✓ Ribbon or twine

Tie shut and give it to someone you love. Cute!

1 Trace the box template and cut a pattern from paper. Stick the pattern to the wrong side of some patterned card and cut out the shape.

2 Gently score along all the dotted fold lines and fold them forward like this

3 Now put double-sided sticky tape on the right side of the four side tabs.

4 Fold up and secure the little tabs to the front. Now do the same with the side panels of the box.
Fold in the top tabs of the side panels, then fold the lid forward and the little flap tucks inside.

5 Finish by tucking a tiny piece of tissue inside, and pop in your sweets — we filled ours with tiny Smarties, but you could use a Rolo or Malteser instead.

sweeties ⟶
yum!

BACK

SIDE

FRONT

LID

SIDE

TEMPLATE

25

DIY Pineapple Pot!

This pencil pot will brighten up your room!

You'll need:

- Jam jar (wash and dry it first!)
- PVA glue
- A paintbrush
- White tissue paper
- Scissors
- Yellow and green paint
- Brown felt-tip pen

1 Paint a layer of glue on your jar and leave to dry (this will help the tissue paper stick). Cut the tissue paper into squares and stick them to the jar with glue. Leave to dry and continue adding layers until you can't see light shining through the jar.

2 Add some colour with the yellow paint — you might need a couple of layers so that none of the tissue paper shows through. Don't forget to add a band of green paint at the top of the jar!

3 Finish by adding V shapes all over the jar, then fill with pencils, pens or anything else you like — it looks best if they're all green!

If you want to turn your pencils green, add some paint or nail polish or wrap in green washi tape — so easy!

Beautiful Brooch!

Here's how to make this cute Clover—inspired accessory!

You'll need:

- Green felt
- Scissors
- Needle
- Thread (we've used pink so you can see the stitching, but green or black is best)
- Brooch back or safety pin

1 Use the template to cut four shapes from the felt.

template

2 Run the thread through all four pieces like this — make a stitch at the back, a stitch at the front, then a stitch to join the next shape.

3 Carefully pull all the shapes together and add a couple of stitches to secure. Stitch on a brooch back and you'll have a beautiful clover accessory! ⭐

WHY NOT Add a blob of fabric glue and some sparkly beads or sequins to the centre?

Tilly's Floral Crown Tutorial!

Follow these simple steps to make this beautiful floral head band!

Here's what you'll need...

Floristry tape

A selection of artificial flowers — pick whatever colours you fancy!

A hairband

A pair of scissors

What to do...

1 Trim the parts of the flowers you want to use — you only need small pieces! Hold the flower against the headband and wrap the tape around the stem to attach it.

2 Continue wrapping pieces of flowers round the band, making sure that you include a variety of different colours to make it look really pretty!

3 Wrap flowers around the band until you come to the other end. Remember to make sure there's an even amount of flowers all the way around. Now you've got a beautiful floral crown fit for a bridesmaid!

TIP!

You can try making a crown using flowers from your garden — just ask permission first!

Melissa's Pretty Posies

Freshen up your bedroom with my tissue paper flowers!

You'll need:
- Tissue paper in two different shades
- Scissors
- Green craft sticks

1. Cut four 15cm x 15cm squares of tissue paper from the darker colour and two squares of the same size from the lighter colour.

2. Stack the squares with the lighter sheets on top and fold the tissue paper in a concertina style, making folds around 1cm wide.

3. Wind a craft stick round the centre and twist to secure. Cut a rounded edge and then cut 3cm slits towards the centre.

4. Unfold one side of the flower and gently tease apart the layers of tissue paper, fluffing the petals as you go.

why not? Make some flowers in different colours!

5. Pop your finished flower in a vase or create a gorgeous garland to string across your headboard!

Pixel Pres

Glam and Girlie Pixel Hair Bow

So cute!

1 Follow this pattern to create the bow outline.

2 Fill with your friend's favourite colours like this.

Fashionista Friend Chevron Necklace

A cool gift for a stylish BFF!

1 Follow these patterns to make a single chevron pendant or a zig-zag necklace.

Kind and Creative Heart Hanger

This token of love is perfect for your friend!

1 Lay out your beads in a heart shape like this. Add a little extra bead in the centre so you can add a ribbon hanger.

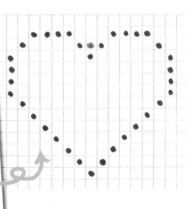

2 Fill the centre — this rainbow effect looks lovely.

ents

To make these gifts you'll need:

- Fuse beads
- Square peg board
- Non-stick baking paper

③ Now ask an adult to iron the beads so they fuse together – follow the instructions on the bead pack.

④ Glue a hair slide to the back and leave it to dry.

Now it's ready to wear! Make lots to match your favourite outfits.

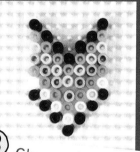

② Fill with your friend's favourite colours like this.

③ Choose the colours you like to create the rows, then fuse the beads.

Thread through some coloured string or embroidery thread to make the necklace – metallic thread would look good too.

③ Fuse the beads and let them cool.

④ Thread some coloured string or embroidery thread through the centre bead to make the hanger.

A sweet gift for a brilliant bestie!

Why not? Add some thread and gems too.

Hetty's Silhouette Sun Catcher

Make a magical sun catcher!

You'll need:

- Scissors
- Card
- Coloured tissue paper
- Glue stick
- Sticky tac or ribbon

1. Cut out page 93 and stick it to card. Very carefully, follow the dashed lines to cut out the template. You may want to ask an adult to help you.

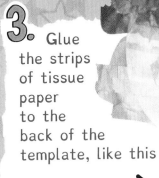

3. Glue the strips of tissue paper to the back of the template, like this

2. Gently tear strips of tissue paper, around 20cm long. It doesn't matter if the edges are rough — this only adds to the effect.

4. When the glue has dried, snip off the excess tissue paper. When you turn your template over it should look like this.

5. You can use sticky tac or ribbon to fix or hang your sun catcher to your bedroom window.

Beaker Sneakers!

These trainers are the best shoes EVER
— they've got my face on them!

You'll need:

★ A pair of canvas sneakers

★ Fabric paint in peach, black and pink

★ Black ric-rac (I used just over 2 metres)

★ Fabric glue

★ Scissors

Always ask an adult for help when crafting!

1. Lightly sketch my head in pencil — you'll be covering this, so don't worry about being too neat.

2. Paint my face using peach fabric paint, then leave to dry before adding details. If you're not too neat, you can use a marker pen instead.

3. Use fabric glue to stick strips of ric-rac round my head. You may need to add some extra to fill in the gaps.

4. Paint the rest of your shoes red and blue to match my outfit — once dry, your shoes are ready to wear!

5-MINUTE MODELLING CLAY

It's easy to make! Here's how...

You'll need:

- 180g Cornflour
- 360g Bicarbonate of soda
- 280ml Water

1. Put the cornflour and bicarbonate of soda into a saucepan. Mix with a little of the water to make a paste. Now gradually add the remaining water to get a milky liquid — don't worry about lumps!

2. Ask an adult to help you heat the liquid on a medium heat, stirring all the time. Little bubbles will start to appear round the edges, but don't let the mix boil.

3. Keep stirring and after a few minutes the mix will start to thicken. When it's thick and doughy like this, it's ready!

Tip the dough mix on to a surface lightly dusted with cornflour. Cover with a damp tea towel and leave to cool.

4. Knead the cool clay until it's smooth and silky. Now you can start rolling, cutting and modelling!

Look what we made — just use cookie cutters to make shapes and tie them together with pretty string or ribbon. You can add decoration too!

TIP!

To dry and harden the clay, leave it in a warm place for a couple of days or place in the oven at 100°C (100°F/gas mark ¾).

After 30 minutes in the oven, turn off the heat and leave for two hours. If the clay is still soft, bake again for another 30 minutes — don't let it brown or burn.

DOODLE & DRAW

So many fun things to sketch, colour and draw! Grab your best pens and start doodling and designing now!

Sketch your fave JW character here!

SIBLINGS

Write about your pesky siblings here!

DRAW YOUR SIBLINGS HERE!

❝ That's the best thing about my sister — she's always there. ❞
MARTY, *THE WORST THING ABOUT MY SISTER.*

Name: ....
Age: ....

Name: ....
Age: ....

Name: ....
Age: ....

Name: ....
AGE: ....

Don't have a sibling? Why not draw and describe your dream brother or sister here!

Name: ....
My imaginary sibling likes:
....
....
We would be:
☐ BEST FRIENDS
☐ DEADLIEST ENEMIES

START HERE!

Draw yourself here or stick on your fave photo!

GRANDPARENTS

My nan means the world to me. Do you have a nan or grandpa? Stick a photo here!

❝ Nan and I were ever so happy, just the two of us together. ❞
ELSIE, *QUEENIE*

Did You Know?
Ga was my pet name for my lovely grandmother. My grandad was Gongon.

People all over the world have different names for their grandparents...

UK:
Nana/Grandma/Gran
Papa/Grandpa/Grandad

RUSSIA:
Babushka
Dedushka

GERMANY:
Oma
Opa

ITALY:
Nonna
Nonno

CHINA:
Nai–Nai
Yeh–Yeh

PARENTS

DRAW YOUR PARENTS OR CARERS HERE!

Or write about who takes care of you!

Now jot down all the things you ♥ about them!

MEET ME!

this section, then move round the page
p you write a story about your family.

What's the one wish you'd make for your family?

6 6 I think you're the most magic mother in the whole wide world. 9 9
DOLPHIN, _THE ILLUSTRATED MUM_

ame: Hannah

born:

ar sign is: Leo

PETS

Have you got a special pet? Draw your animal friend (or friends!) below!

Now design a special ID tag for your pet! Don't forget to add its name!

Don't have a pet of your own? Why not write a story about your dream furry friend instead?

Pet's name:

Fave treat:

Pet's name:

Fave treat:

9 9 I would always pat any friendly dog I found and make up imaginary dogs when I played... 9 9
JACQUELINE WILSON,
JACKY DAYDREAM

Nick's Picture

It's full of tiny details with something new to spot each time you look. Follow the tips and YOU can do it too!

Decide on a
loved drawin
streets whe

Start at the bottom left of your page and draw one object or person. Now add a few more things surrounding them. Nick used signs, prams, plants and clocks amongst all the people.

Then just keep adding to fill more and more of the page. It's best to do a little bit every day instead of trying to finish it all in one go.

Prompt!

...e was only 10?

...for your scene. Nick... shopping centres or... could add lots and... stuff.

You can make up a scene or draw somewhere you know well. Why not take some photos for inspiration? Here are a few ideas –

- A crowded beach
- A funfair
- A flower garden
- Under the sea

Draw in pencil first and, when you're happy with your sketch, start to ink in the outlines.

Nick drew so much he had to tape more sheets of paper to his picture!

Now it's time to add the finishing details with colour or black and white shading.

How To Draw Young Hetty!

I'll show you how!

1. Use a pencil to outline Hetty's head and shoulders, making sure to include her ears and cap!

2. Pencil in two little dots for eyes, a wide U shape for her button nose, a wonky smile and a little line to show where her chin is. Draw two plaits coming from behind her ears, disappearing behind her back.

3. Sketch some lines for her fringe and criss-crossing lines over her plaits to make them look more realistic! Don't forget the collar and sleeves of her dress!

4. Go back over your pencil with a black pen or marker, and copy the picture to add some colour.

Drawing Hetty's eyebrows and mouth pointing downwards will make her look annoyed and angry! Why not try some other facial expressions?

How To Draw
Grown-up Hetty!

1. Start by drawing an egg shape, with the larger end at the top. Draw a round bun on the top of Hetty's head, and include her ears and strands of hair at the sides.

2. Draw two rectangles for Hetty's collar just underneath her face, then sketch her bodice and arms. Add more hair at the back of her head.

3. Draw two lines coming down from her jacket and join them at the bottom to make her skirt. Include button details on her jacket, lines for her fringe, and her right hand.

4. Add Hetty's other hand and her face and dress details. Colour in your drawing using a nice orangey-red for Hetty's fiery hair and a lemon-yellow for her dress!

Why not design Hetty a new dress!

Doodle Challenge!

On your marks, get set... doodle!

What do you see when you look at a circle? Is it a clock face? A cookie? A planet? You've got 30 minutes to think up as many circular designs as you can! Why not challenge your friends to see who can come up with the most designs — and the most imaginative ones!

The Official Jacqueline Wilson Mag

Speedy Sketches!

Floss's Toffee Apple

Why not stick some red glitter to Floss's toffee apple? Mmmm!

Beauty's Bunny Biscuits

Use a slightly darker shade to colour the outline to give your bunny biscuits a 3D effect!

Jacky's books are filled with scrummy—licious descriptions of food! I'm getting hungry just thinking about them...

Draw Your Dream Dinner!

Would it be...

A towering sundae with lashings of cream and chocolate — dessert for dinner rules!

A sophisticated 10—course banquet, of course! You've always wanted to try caviar, darling...

Eggs, sausage and beans — breakfast is the most important meal of the day, so you should get to have it twice!

Draw your yummiest concoction here

I'd pick a chicken dish, followed by a gooseberry crumble and cream for pudding!

Nick's Arty Tips!

I'll help you with your artwork issues!

I'm not very good at drawing — how can I get better?

If you draw with a good strong black line (try using a black fibre-tip pen or a very soft pencil) your drawings will instantly look more confident. Also, try to finish your pictures, even if you're not quite sure about them. If you persevere, you might be in for a nice surprise when you get to the end.

What are the best things to have in an art kit?

It's fun to try all sorts of art materials if you're able, to discover what really suits you best. I think softer (B) pencils are better for sketching than hard (H) pencils. And a soft rubber won't damage your paper like a hard one can. A pocket-sized sketchbook is a great thing to carry with you in case you see anything interesting to draw when you're out and about.

What are some easy things that I could draw if I'm not very good at it?

My book *How to Draw the World of Jacqueline Wilson* has tips on easy ways to draw all kinds of things in addition to Jacqueline's characters.

HOW TO DRAW
THE WORLD OF
JACQUELINE WILSON
Nick Sharratt

My arty dilemma is...

_____

_____

To solve it, I'm going to...

_____

_____

Ultimate Quiz Master

Show off your superior Jacqueline Wilson knowledge and discover the inner you!

THE NAME GAME!

What would you call your quiz club?
Find your age in the list below.
If you're aged 10 or over, add the numbers
together until you get just one digit!

1. Let's Get Quizzical
2. Trivia Troupe
3. The Dream Team
4. The Smartie Squad
5. The Galaxy Girls
6. Fan Favourites
7. Quiz Queens
8. The Clever Clogs
9. The Wise Quacks

The Ultimate JW Quiz!

How much do you really know about Jacky and her books?

JUST JACKY!

How much do you know about Jacky?

1. Jacky was born in...

Bath ☐   Dundee ☐   Kingston Upon Thames ☐

2. She used to work on a magazine called...

Bunty ☐   Jackie ☐   Twinkle ☐

3. Her pet cat's name is...

Jacob ☐   Jimmy ☐   Jackson ☐

4. The TB book Jacky and Nick Sharratt first worked together on was...

The Dare Game ☐   *Starring Tracy Beaker* ☐   *The Story of Tracy Beaker* ☑

5. As a child, Jacky called her Grandmother...

Gan-Gan ☐   Ga ☑   Nana ☐

HISTORY MYSTERIES!

How much do you know about the books Jacky set in the past?

1. What was the name of the circus in *Diamond*?

A) Beppo's ☐   B) Barnum's ☐   C) Tanglefield's ☐

2. Who buys Hetty Feather a journal to write in?

A) Ida ☐   B) Miss Smith ☐   C) Madame Adeline ☐

3. What did Clover call the little doll she made in *Clover Moon*?

A) Anne Boleyn ☐   B) Hyacinth ☐   C) Thelma ☐

4. Which of these books is set in the Edwardian period?

A) *The Lottie Project* ☐   B) *Emerald Star* ☐   C) *Opal Plumstead* ☐

5. Who ends up in Milltree Hospital with tuberculosis?

A) Elsie ☐   B) Megs ☐   C) Sapphire Battersea ☐

WHICH SIS?

Can you figure out the character from her siblings?

1. Who has a sister called Pearl?

_ O _ _ E

2. Sunset's little sister is...

_ W _ _ _ I _

3. Who has an adoptive big brother called Will?

_ _ O _ _ T

4. Which Diamond sister is missing?

Martine, Jude, Rochelle and _ I _ _ E

5. Vita, Maxie and _ M _ L _ live in their grandmother's house.

TRICKY TITLES!

Can you remember which books feature these characters?

1. Two best friends called Matilda.

_ E _ _/_/_ R _ _ _ S _ _ I _

2. An abandoned baby called April.

_ _ S _ _ _ N/_ _ B _

3. A boy called Tim and his summer at an Adventure Camp!

_ L _ _ _ _ A _ G _ _

4. The Alphabet Club: Amy, Bella, Chloe, Daisy and Emily.

SLEEPOVERS

5. A very quiet girl called Lizzie.

_ I _ _ _ E/_ I _ _ O _ _ _

ANSWERS:

TRICKY TITLES! — 1. Rent A Bridesmaid, 2. Dustbin Baby, 3. Cliffhanger, 4. Sleepovers, 5. Lizzie Zipmouth.

WHICH SIS? — 1. Jodie, 2. Sweetie, 3. Violet, 4. Dixie, 5. Emily.

HISTORY MYSTERIES! — 1. C, 2. B, 3. A, 4. C, 5. A.

JUST JACKY! — 1. Bath, 2. Jackie, 3. Jacob, 4. The Story of Tracy Beaker, 5. Ga

SCORES! ➔

0–6
Oh, dear, you've got lots to learn about Jacky's books — but that just gives you a good excuse to go read them all! Hit the library and get started!

7–13
You know quite a lot about all things JW, but there's definitely room for improvement! Jog your memory by re-reading some of her older books!

14–20
Super-fan alert! You're totally clued up when it comes to Jacky and her books — in fact, there's very little you *don't* know! You get a gold star!

51

LUCKY CHARM!

Pick the answer that sounds most like you to find out which charm will bring you luck!

1. YOU SEE A BLACK CAT!

A. You cross the road — black cats are bad luck!

B. You stop to say hello!

2. WHICH IS WORSE?

A. Opening an umbrella indoors.

B. Putting shoes on a table.

3. YOU STEP OUTSIDE AND STRAIGHT INTO A PUDDLE!

A. Oops — better pay attention next time!

B. I'm going to have bad luck all day!

4. YOU WOULD RATHER...

A. Walk under a ladder.

B. Walk over a crack on the pavement.

5. YOU SEE A PENNY ON THE GROUND!

A. You pick it up and keep it in your pocket!

B. You pass it on to someone else for luck!

MOSTLY A — FOUR LEAF CLOVER

The chances of finding a four-leaf clover are 10,000 to one — so finding one makes you especially lucky! If you don't find one on your first try, why not make one out of card or material? Carry it wherever you go and good luck will follow!

MOSTLY B — LUCKY DICE

When we roll a dice we leave the outcome to chance — which is why rolling a high number is associated with luck! Roll your dice each morning until you reach a number 10 or above for good luck!

MAGIC BLACK CAT!

I'm goo[d] luck!

You will always be surrounded by true friends!

LUCK!

Find out how lucky you are with Floss and Rose!

Close your eyes and put your finger over the black cat. When you open your eyes, see which duck your eyes are drawn to first to get your lucky fortune!

You are more talented than you know — now is the time to try something new!

Your luck is about to change — a good deed never goes unnoticed!

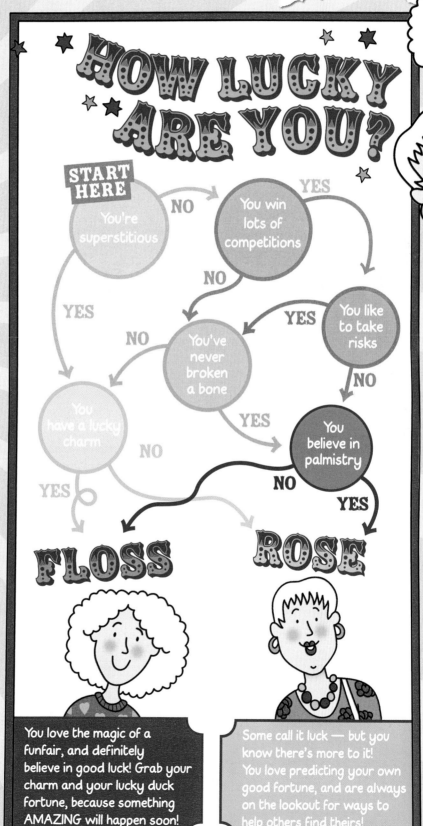

HOW LUCKY ARE YOU?

START HERE

You're superstitious — NO → You win lots of competitions — YES → You like to take risks

You're superstitious — YES ↓

You win lots of competitions — NO → You've never broken a bone

You like to take risks — NO → You believe in palmistry

You've never broken a bone — NO → You have a lucky charm

You've never broken a bone — YES → You believe in palmistry

You have a lucky charm — YES ↓ — NO ↓

FLOSS

ROSE

You believe in palmistry — NO ↓ — YES ↓

FLOSS
You love the magic of a funfair, and definitely believe in good luck! Grab your charm and your lucky duck fortune, because something AMAZING will happen soon!

ROSE
Some call it luck — but you know there's more to it! You love predicting your own good fortune, and are always on the lookout for ways to help others find theirs!

53

Blush Or Butterfly?

Follow the arrows to find your personality match!

START

Making new friends is easy-peasy!

NO →

YES →

 You quickly brush off cringes.

You'd rather eat WORMS than read aloud in class!

NO → You can be a bit timid.

You get a ticking off for being a chatterbox.

NO

YES

YES

You were born to be a star!

YES

YES

You'd pick a book over a party any day!

NO

YES

You're such a day-dreamer!

YES

NO

You're the queen of good gossip!

NO

YES

YES

You find it hard to speak up in a group.

NO

YES

You like to make people LOL!

NO

NO

You're really popular.

YES

OH-SO-SHY!

SOCIAL BUTTERFLY!

Aww, you're a shy little caterpillar waiting to bloom into a beautiful butterfly — just like Beauty, Violet and Mandy!

OH-SO-SHY!

Be Yourself!
You don't have to impress anyone or pretend to be something you're not. You're totally amazing, you just need to come out of your shell now and then and let everyone else see the real you!

TOP TIPS!

It's OK to be shy — new social situations can be scary! But practice makes perfect, so get into the butterfly mind-set and dare yourself to be more social.

Start off small! Get used to talking in front of people — try answering a question in class when you'd usually hide, or give someone a compliment.

Ask lots of questions! They can keep a conversation going and fill up awkward silences – and the other person will do most of the talking! Success!

Join an after-school club to meet some new people. You'll already have something in common to talk about to help break the ice!

You're super-sociable, confident and happiest when you're the centre of attention, just like Melissa, Magda and Elsa!

SOCIAL BUTTERFLY!

Be Balanced!
Take some ME time — busy bees and social butterflies need time to themselves, too! Try a nice bubble bath and curl up with a good book. Ahh, bliss!

TOP TIPS!

We know you like to chat, but show your friends that you can be just as good at listening - your friendships will be even more rock solid as a result!

Having lots of friends can be tough and some people might start to feel ignored in the crowd, so pay some extra attention to your besties!

Take a step back once in a while and let others shine — why not pass along your social know-how and encourage a shy friend to come out of their shell?

Just Chill!
As long as you love yourself, and have friends that think the same, you'll be OK!

Your bedroom is:

FILLED WITH TOYS

VINTAGE-STYLE

A BIT OF A MESS!

COVERED IN YOUR DRAWINGS

WHERE YOU GO TO DAYDREAM

You're best described as:

ADVENTUROUS

FUNNY

IMAGINATIVE

SENSITIVE

ENERGETIC

You're happiest when:

YOU'RE ENJOYING YOUR HOBBY

YOU'VE GOT AN AUDIENCE!

YOU MAKE OTHERS SMILE

YOU'RE WITH YOUR FAMILY

SOMEONE GIVES YOU A HUG

MOSTLY
You are Hetty

Brave, heroic and *never* afraid to say exactly what's on your mind! Like Hetty, you enjoy the limelight. No one could ever mistake you for shy!

MOSTLY
You are Lottie

You're lively, funny, and a real homebody at heart. You really cherish quality time with your family, whether it's going out for the day, baking, or just chilling on a Sunday.

MOSTLY
You are Elsie

What a little daydreamer you are! You're bursting with great story ideas and inspiration! Your funny stories and tales always have your friends in fits of giggles.

MOSTLY
You are Opal

Just like Opal, you have a warm and sensitive personality — and bags of artistic talent! You're always happiest when you're creating something new and exciting.

MOSTLY
You are Diamond

Such a sweetheart! You're a cuddly character, with a big heart and an even bigger smile! You love sleepovers with your besties and hugs with your loved ones.

What's Your Pet Personality?

Tick the boxes to find your purr—fect animal match!

Which JW character are you most like?

☑ Gemma   ☑ Verity   ☑ Beauty

Tick the three phrases that sound most like you.

☑ I never ever tell secrets.

☐ It takes me a–g–e–s to choose the perfect outfit!

☑ Best thing about sleepovers? Midnight feasts!

☑ I spend most of my free time with my BF.

☑ Cuddles are the best thing ever!

☐ I like painting my nails and trying out new hairstyles.

☑ I'm full of beans and bursting with energy!

☑ I love to curl up with a cosy blanket and a good book.

☐ I could spend all day in my comfy bed.

Pick your three favourite pictures.

Now count up how much you got of each colour...

☐ Pink ☑ Purple ☐ Orange

MOSTLY PINK

Cat

Just like an elegant kitty, you're confident, glamorous and sophisti–cat–ed! There's nothing you enjoy more than a pampering session or giving your bestie a mini makeover. You're very inquisitive (maybe just a teensy bit nosey!) and you love to chat, which can sometimes land you in trouble!

JW books you might like:

MOSTLY PURPLE

Bunny

You're a sensitive soul, with a gentle and caring nature. You're a special friend, too: you'd never blab a secret and you're always there to lend a helping hand. Sleepovers at your house are the best — you're the perfect hostess whenever your besties come to stay!

JW books you might like:

MOSTLY ORANGE Dog

Like a loyal pooch, you stick by your friends and family through thick and thin! You have such a lovable nature — everyone wants to be your BF! Outdoors activities like sports, gardening and building dens are definitely your kind of thing... you don't mind getting your hands mucky!

JW books you might like:

TB* or Not TB?

Are you Tracy's terrible twin or her total opposite?

Ouch! You've fallen down and skinned your knee — how did you do this?

- **Playing footie with the boys — you're totally ace at tackling!** ☑
- Playing jumping rope with your BFFs. ☐

You have a test you haven't studied for. Do you:

- Cram in some last-minute studying all through lunch. ☐
- **Wing it — you're clever enough to know all the answers anyway!** ☑

Someone dares you to eat a wriggly worm... do you?

- **Of course! You'd never back down from a challenge!** ☐
- Eww, no way! Plus, dares are sooo juvenile. ☑

What's your role in the school play?

- **Obviously, I'm the star of the show — I was born to be centre stage!** ☐
- **I hate the spotlight. I'd prefer to do something creative behind the scenes!** ☑

You've just woken up from a scary nightmare. Do you:

- Cry like a baby and need a hug from mum? ☑
- Sniff a bit, but only because your hay fever's playing up? ☐

You accidentally broke your sister's toy. Do you:

- Own up and apologise — it's the right thing to do. ☐
- Make up a tall tale and try to get away with it? ☑

MOSTLY PINK!

Tremendous twin sister alert! We're like two peas in a pod!

HALF & HALF!

I see a lot of myself in you — but you're a bit too sensible to get in too much Tracy Trouble!

MOSTLY BLUE!

You're not a bit like me — in fact, we're total opposites. Scoff your weight in egg and chips and maybe one day you'll be as cool as I am!

Check the Tracy-o-meter!

STAR BAKER

Head to the kitchen and treat your family and friends to some delicious treats!

What's your best bake? Stick a picture of it here!

BISCUIT'S COOKIE CAKES!

Make these massive biscuits!

You'll need:

- Two sponge cakes (we used a shop-bought Victoria sponge and split the layers)
- Icing sugar
- Food colouring (we used pink, purple and yellow)
- Buttercream icing — add some hot chocolate powder to get a cookie colour
- Chocolate chips
- Toothpicks

Giant Party Ring!

Make a huge version of Jacky's favourite biscuit!

1. Cut out a circle from the centre of your sponge cake. We used the mouth of a pint glass as a guide.

2. Mix up some water icing in your chosen colours, then spread on the cake rings. While the icing is wet, use a contrast colour to drizzle lines across the cake like this.

3. Use a toothpick to drag lines through the icing like this. Make sure they all go in the same direction!

Now you can wow your friends with a super-sized biccie!

Colossal Cookie!

Don't let any cake go to waste — use the centres you cut out to make giant cookies!

4. Spread the cake with buttercream icing, then place large chocolate chips all over it! Done!

ASK AN ADULT TO HELP IN THE KITCHEN!

Butterfly Brunch!

Food just got flutterly fantastic!

You'll need:

Your favourite breakfast bites — we used pancakes, grapes, clementines, strawberries, banana and chocolate spread!

Use scissors to cut a pancake in half and trim to look like butterfly wings. Place on a plate and add chopped fruit to create pretty markings!

Arrange two segments of clementine like this and add a body made of grape or strawberry!

Slice a banana and arrange the discs like this — you can add slices of grapes to decorate!

Butterfly Treats!

Make a sweet version for a special treat.

WHY NOT? Have a butterfly decorating party with your besties!

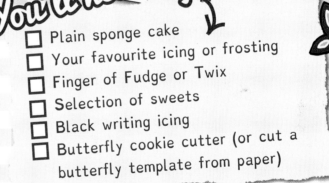

Cut a strawberry into slices and then each slice in half. Arrange like this to make pretty little butterflies!

Cut grapes in half lengthways and arrange around half a grape cut widthways. Add a stalk made of chocolate spread and place some more cut grapes for leaves.

Why not?

Send us a pic of your butterfly brunch to jwmag@dcthomson.co.uk

You'll need:

- ☐ Plain sponge cake
- ☐ Your favourite icing or frosting
- ☐ Finger of Fudge or Twix
- ☐ Selection of sweets
- ☐ Black writing icing
- ☐ Butterfly cookie cutter (or cut a butterfly template from paper)

1. Use your cutter or template to cut butterfly shapes from sponge.

2. Ice the tops of the butterflies and decorate with sweets.

3. Cut each butterfly in half along the centre to create two separate wings.

4. Place your Fudge or Twix in the centre of a plate and place your wings at the side.

5. Now add a sweetie head and antennae — we used chocolate sticks and mini beans for these. Draw on a face with writing icing. Done!

Beaker Bento Bite!

Make your very own Tracy Beaker lunchtime treat!

You'll need:

- Slices of white and brown bread
- Scissors
- Cucumber
- Red pepper

1 Use scissors to cut an oval from a brown slice of bread, making the outer edge wavy for Tracy's hair. Cut a smaller oval from the centre, with two notches for her ears.

2 Using the bread you cut from the centre as a guide, cut Tracy's face from a slice of white bread.

3 Fit the face shape inside the hair and add Tracy's face using cucumber skin for her eyes, nose and mouth, and red pepper for her t-shirt and cheeks!

You'd never get tasty treats like THIS in the rotten Dumping Ground!

A bento box is a Japanese home-packed lunch — usually filled with rice and veggies and arranged in a pretty way! Check out these cute creations for inspiration!

Biscuit Designer!

Jazz up plain biscuits with bold and beautiful icing!

You'll need:

- Biscuits (we used digestives)
- Icing in different colours (use writing icing pens for ease!)

1. Ice your biscuits and leave them to set for a bit before the next step — overnight is best.

2. Go crazy with colour-clash designs! Here are some of ours —

Doodle And Design!

Grab your pens and decorate this biscuit your way!

Opal's Perfect Picnic!

Impress your friends with these delicious treats!

✿ Pretty Little Choccies!

These cute choccies are super-easy to make!

Perfect for picnics!

You'll need:
- Cake sprinkles
- White chocolate
- A chocolate or ice cube mould (we got our mould for £1 from ASDA!)

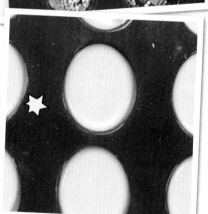

1. Place some cake sprinkles in the bottom of your chocolate mould. Don't completely cover the bottom as the chocolate will need to get in-between the sprinkles.

2. Melt the chocolate and pour into the moulds. Use a teaspoon to help you carefully measure out just enough for each one.

3. Leave to chill and then pop out of their cases once they've hardened — yummy!

Petite Parasols!

These mini parasols will add a touch of pizazz to your party!

1. Fold a cupcake case in half three times, then trim the edge like this to create a frilly brim. Snip a tiny bit from the pointy edge of the case to fit your straw through — remember it'll be much bigger when you unfold it!

2. Unfold the cupcake case and use a felt-tip pen to lightly colour the edge of one section. Then, use a paintbrush and water to bleed the colour from the edge to the centre of the case to give a faded effect. Repeat for all the other sections of the case and leave to dry.

Lovely Lemonade!

This pretty pink lemonade is sooo refreshing!

You'll need:

- 100g caster sugar
- 1 litre of water
- 4 lemons
- 40g raspberries, crushed

1. Place the sugar in a large jug and pour the water on top, stirring to dissolve the sugar.

2. Squeeze the juice from the lemons into a smaller jug and add the juice from the raspberries.

3. Pour the lemon and raspberry juice into the larger jug — taste as you go and add more sugar or lemon juice, if needed!

TIP! Increase or decrease the recipe easily — just use 25g of sugar and 10g of raspberries per lemon!

TIP! Replace half the water with sparkling water for a fizzy lemonade!

3. Fold the case in half three times, then unfold — this will help the case flare out like an umbrella — and place on a straw. Fold one of the sections over the next one like this, securing with glue or double-sided tape. Once dry, pop in your drink and enjoy!

Flutter Fairy

Sparkle Wands

Enchanted pink nibbles you'll love!

You'll need:
★ Pink wafer biscuits
★ Icing sugar
★ Sprinkles

1 Make up a bowl of icing following the instructions on the pack.

2 Dip the wafers in halfway and tap off any excess.

3 Quickly shake on sprinkles before the icing sets!

Flutter Fairy Cakes

So delicate and pretty!

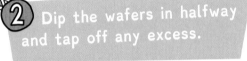

You'll need:
❀ Pack of plain cupcakes
❀ Frosting
❀ Sugar balls

1 Ask an adult to help you slice off the top of each cupcake.

2 Carefully cut each top in half to create two wing shapes and set to one side.

3 Top each cake with frosting. Gently press on two wings and add a sprinkle of pretty sugar balls.

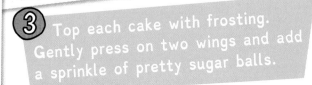

Tea Party!

Treat your family and friends to some spellbinding snacks!

Fairy Bread

You'll need:
* White bread
* Chocolate spread
* Sprinkles
* Cookie cutter

1 Spread a slice of bread with the chocolate spread.

2 Add a layer of colourful sprinkles.

This Australian snack is a real sweet treat!

3 Use the cookie cutter to make a window in a second slice of bread and place this on top of the other slice.

4 Cut off the crusts to make a neat sandwich.

Toadstool Treats

1 Ask an adult to slice off the very top of the strawberries.

You'll need:
* Strawberries
* Marshmallows
* White icing pen
* Skewers or cake pop sticks

Magical and oh-so-tasty!

2 Push the stick through a marshmallow and top with an upside-down strawberry.

3 Dot on white icing spots to complete your tasty toadstool!

Always ask an adult before using kitchen equipment.

Make YUMMY Hot Chocolate!

The perfect hot chocolate for a chilly day!

You'll need:

- ○ 450ml whole milk
- ○ 100g milk chocolate, finely chopped or grated
- ○ 75ml single cream

Serves 2

Method

Ask an adult to help you warm 150ml of milk in a pan on medium heat and stir in the chocolate. Once it has melted, whisk in the remaining milk and cream and warm through.

Why Not?

Add some tasty toppings!

- ✓ Whipped cream
- ✓ Marshmallows
- ✓ Chocolate sprinkles
- ○ A scoop of ice cream can add a cool kick to your hot choccy!

Add these ingredients to the pan after the chocolate has melted.

Flavour Station

NICE AND NUTTY	CARAMEL CHOCCY	PEANUT BUTTER CUP
1½ tbsp Nutella A pinch of salt (optional)	1½ tbsp caramel sauce	1 tbsp peanut butter

Perfectly Puzzling!

Sharpen your pencils! These puzzles will boggle your brain!

Unscramble these letters to reveal a secret message from Jacky!

I nut day coo

Net ___ ___ ___!

Carnival Spectacular!

Roll up for tons of fairground fun!

FLOSS'S LUCKY DUCKIES!

Pick a duck to find your lucky fortune!

1 An old foe will surprise you with a good deed!

2 A change of circumstances will bring positive results.

3 The best things in life are free — and are heading your way!

6 You will hear of an exciting opportunity soon!

4 The stress of a test will be eased with a helping hand.

5 A special occasion is just around the corner.

9 Helping others will bring many rewards.

7 Your friend has a secret to share with you.

8 A disagreement will be sorted quickly.

HOW TO CHOOSE A DUCK

Count the number of letters in your full name. Keep adding the numbers together until you get 9 or less.

For example: if your name was

NATALIE SMITH...

$7 + 5 = 11$
$1 + 1 = 2$

ROSE'S MYSTIC RUNES

Decode the riddles to reveal JW secrets!

A-ᚨ	J-✳	S-ᛋ
B-ᛒ	K-ᚲ	T-ᛏ
C-ᛐ	L-ᚱ	U-ᚾ
D-ᛘ	M-ᛘ	V-ᚢ
E-ᛗ	N-ᚼ	W-ᛈ
F-ᚦ	O-ᚠ	X-ᛣ
G-ᚷ	P-ᚴ	Y-ᛉ
H-ᚺ	Q-ᛉ	Z-ᛣ
I-ᛁ	R-ᚱ	

1. The name of Jacky's 100th book:

ᚠᚨᛐᛏ ᛐᚱᚾᚨᛋᛏᛘᚨᚾ

2. A JW character with fiery red hair and a temper to match!

ᚺᛗᛏᛏᚨ ᚠᛗᚨᛏᚺᛗᚱ

3. Sunset's spoilt younger sister:

ᛋᚴᛗᛗᛏᛁᛗ

4. The VIP who visits Elsie Kettle during her stay in hospital:

ᛏᚺᛗ ᚴᚾᛗᛗᚾ

5. Em's favourite author in Clean Break:

✳ᛗᚾᚾᚨ ᛈᛁᚱᚱᛁᚨᛘᛋ

6. Rosalind, Robbie, Smash and Maudie's favourite place to visit:

ᚠᛉᛋᚺᚨᛏᛏ ᛈᚠᚠᛘᛋ

SUSAN'S MAGIC SQUARES

Fit the numbers into the grid – each line must add up to the Magic Number, in all directions.

⭐⭐⭐ HOW TO PLAY ⭐⭐⭐

For example: **Magic Number is 15**
Use these numbers: 1, 4, 6, 7, 8, 9

2		
	5	3

➡️

2	9	4
7	5	3
6	1	8

Now you try!

Magic Number is 27

Use these numbers: 5, 6, 7, 10, 11, 13

		12
	9	
		8

Psammead's Brain

Can you outsmart a sand fairy? Take these mini quizzes to f

I Wish...

I grant the best wishes, if I do say so myself...

Would you wish...

- ☑ To fly high like a bird
  OR
- ☐ Swim in the deepest ocean?

- ☐ For beautiful looks
  OR
- ☑ Riches beyond belief?

- ☑ For a magical unicorn
  OR
- ☐ A fire-breathing dragon?

- ☑ To be queen for a week
  OR
- ☑ Invisible for a day?

- ☑ To be a famous movie star
  OR
- ☐ A bestselling author?

Cross-fit

Rosalind   Anthea
Robbie   Cyril
Smash   Jane
Maudie   Lamb
Robert

Bogglers

t!

I doubt you'll outwit me!

nundrum

Please fit my human acquaintances into the grid in an orderly fashion.

Riddle Me This!

The riddliest, trickiest challenges I have to offer!

My first letter is in wish but not in fish,
My second is the second in magic.
The third can be found in the middle of mystery,
And the fourth lies at the beginning of enigma.
To find the fifth and final letter you should,
Take Rosalind's initial to complete the word.

The Psammead is afraid of ___water___

Quick Teasers!

1. What can you hold without your hands?

2. What goes up and down stairs without moving?

3. What can honk without using a horn?

Quick Teasers!
1. Your breath.
2. A carpet 3. A goose

Riddle Me This!
The Psammead is afraid of water.

Marty's Messy Maze!

Marty is super-untidy — so Melissa's taught her a lesson by hiding all her stuff! Can you help her through the maze to pick everything up?

Help Marty track down all her belongings!

Spot the difference!

Test yourself with these JW puzzles!

SPOT THE DIFFERENCE
Uh–oh, someone's changed this pretty picture! Can you spot the six differences?

Now circle the changes!

1. Violet's brother befriends her too.

A S E J I M N

_ _ _ _ _ _ _

2. She's Tanya's opposite.

MYNDA

Mandy

3. Daisy longs to be her friend.

IMLYE

_ _ _ _ _

4. Elsa meets her at The Royal Hotel.

AOMIN

5. She's Ellie and Magda's BFF.

ANIDEN

_ _ _ _ _ _

SO MANY PUZZLES!

Pearl's Puzzler!

HOW TO PLAY:

1. Follow Pearl's clues and rearrange the letters at the bottom of the pyramid to create a word in each layer.

2. For each layer of the pyramid, add a letter to make the word longer. For example, if the first word is 'let', add a letter to create the word 'tell', add another letter to create 'telly', etc.

Use my clues to complete the pyramid!

Jodie had hers pierced.

Jodie created the game The Deadly ____.

I hope I get a good ____ in English.

Jodie was in a lot of this in the tower.

How we felt about the badger accident.

Jed is a _____.

STARTING LETTERS

E	N	R	D	A	G	E	R

82

Queenie's Word Quest!

Find all these words in the grid!

Word list:
- Albert
- Blyton
- Coronation
- Elsie
- Gabriel
- Martin
- Mintree
- Nan
- Pyjamas
- Sheila

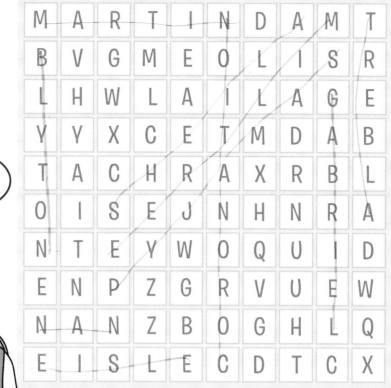

"Can you find me?"

Grid:

M	A	R	T	I	N	D	A	M	T
B	V	G	M	E	O	L	I	S	R
L	H	W	L	A	I	L	A	G	E
Y	Y	X	C	E	T	M	D	A	B
T	A	C	H	R	A	X	R	B	L
O	I	S	E	J	N	H	N	R	A
N	T	E	Y	W	O	Q	U	I	D
E	N	P	Z	G	R	V	U	E	W
N	A	N	Z	B	O	G	H	L	Q
E	I	S	L	E	C	D	T	C	X

Mighty Mart's Word Maker!

How many words can you make out of the letters in the circle? You must include the letter S in each word!

ZAP!

Letter wheel: R, O, U, P, E, E, R, H, S (centre S)

HOW DID YOU DO?

0-4 NOT GREAT! Try finding small words first!

5-8 SO-SO! Keep trying — you can do it!

9+ FANTASTIC! You're a whizz with words!

ANSWERS:
Pearl's Puzzler: Ear, dare, grade, danger, enraged, gardener

Cookie's Conundrum!

Oh, no! Cookie's smudged her recipe! Help her fill in the missing ingredients so she can whip up a batch of beautiful bunny biscuits!

Bunny Bake!

100g softened _ _ _ _ _ _
75g caster sugar
2 _ _ _ _ _ _ _ _
200g plain flour
1/2 tsp mixed
2 tbsp milk

1 Preheat the oven to 180°C and line a baking tray with baking paper.

2 Beat the _ _ _ _ _ _ and sugar in a mixing bowl with a wooden spoon until light and fluffy.

3 Mix in the two _ _ _ _ _ _ _ _ one at a time, then gradually fold in the flour and mixed _ _ _ _ _ _. Slowly add the milk and form a soft dough.

4 Lightly knead your dough on a work surface dusted with flour. Roll it out and use a bunny cookie cutter to cut out the biscuits. Bake in the oven for 12–15 minutes until golden-brown.

All Clued Up!

Solve these clues to find the first ingredient!

My first is in ball, but not in call.
My second is the fourth in flour.
My third is the middle of flutter.
My fourth is in built but not in build.
My fifth is the beginning of the end.
My sixth is the last in baker.

The first missing ingredient is

_ _ _ _ _ _

Grid-tastic!

Put these kitchen items in the grid — the shaded area will spell out the second missing ingredient!

Rolling pin
Knife   Tongs
Bowl   Sieve
Pastry bag
Spoon   Whisk

The second missing ingredient is _ _ _ _ _ _ _ _

All in a Muddle!

Unscramble the final ingredient in the recipe — it's very nice!

CISEP

The third missing ingredient is _ _ _ _ _

CLUE: The first letter is S.

Always get an adult to help in the kitchen!

True or False?

How much do you know about Jacky's childhood?

1. Jacky is an only child. **T** ✓ **F** ✓

2. She wrote her first novel when she was 10 years old. **T** ✓ **F** ✓

3. Her favourite food as a child was pie and mash! **T** ✓ **F** ✓

4. She was born in Bath. **T** ✓ **F** ✓

5. Her favourite subject in school was Art. **T** ✓ **F** ✓

6. Jacky had a cat called Herby when she was small! **T** ✓ **F** ✓

7. Her nickname was Jacky Daydream. **T** ✓ **F** ✓

8. Jacky wanted to be a teacher when she was younger. **T** ✓ **F** ✓

9. Her favourite toy was a dog called Vip! **T** ✓ **F** ✓

10. She had lots of pets when she was younger, just like she does now! **T** ✓ **F** ✓

Grade your guesses!
How many did you get right?

5 or more:
Wow — your answers are spot on! You'll be a JW expert in no time!

Less than 5:
You've still got lots to learn. But don't worry, this annual is packed full of JW facts!

86

ANSWERS: 1. TRUE 2. FALSE 3. FALSE 4. FALSE 5. TRUE 6. FALSE 7. TRUE 8. FALSE 9. TRUE 10. FALSE

Cut Out & Stick!

BOOKS are MAGIC

I READ YA!

All the cut outs you need to create your JW masterpieces!

READING A BOOK

JUST ONE MORE CHAPTER

Decorate your notebooks and pictures with these cut outs!

Aquarius

Write about a treasured possession or a person who means a lot to you.

Pisces

Someone gives you a strange and unusual gift.

Aries

You are invited to appear on TV.

Taurus
You save someone from a very dangerous situation.

Gemini

Write a fabulous party into your tale.

Cancer
You lose something you were asked to take special care of.

Leo

Write an animal into your story.

Virgo
Someone in the story is a very bad influence!

Libra
You find something very rare and valuable.

Scorpio

You can see into the future when you dream.

Sagittarius

Your story needs a sneaky and spiteful bully!

Capricorn
There is a terrible accident!

☆ Aries ☆

YOUR STORY CHARACTER IS
Funny
Clever
Inventive
One of a kind

BUT ALSO
Stubborn
Cheeky
Snooty
Rebellious

☆ Pisces ☆

YOUR STORY CHARACTER IS
Creative
Loyal
Imaginative
A great friend

BUT ALSO
A day-dreamer
Touchy
Lazy
A cry baby

☆ Aquarius ☆

YOUR STORY CHARACTER IS
Generous
Courageous
Enthusiastic
A leader

BUT ALSO
Impatient
Moody
Quick-tempered (tantrum alert!)
Impulsive

☆ Cancer ☆

YOUR STORY CHARACTER IS
Caring
Home-loving
Creative
Forward-thinking

BUT ALSO
Moody (Queen of the sulks!)
Clingy
Unpredictable
Mistrustful

☆ Gemini ☆

YOUR STORY CHARACTER IS
Energetic
Adaptable
Amusing
Talented

BUT ALSO
Sneaky
Restless
Frivolous
Hesitant

☆ Taurus ☆

YOUR STORY CHARACTER IS
Generous
Persistent
Patient
Dependable

BUT ALSO
Self-indulgent
Over-sensitive
Lazy
Secretive

☆ Libra ☆

YOUR STORY CHARACTER IS
Graceful
Friendly
Peaceful
Polite

BUT ALSO
Vain
Indecisive
Silly
Irresponsible

☆ Virgo ☆

YOUR STORY CHARACTER IS
Helpful
Reliable
Observant
Precise

BUT ALSO
Fussy
Cold
Interfering
Suspicious

☆ Leo ☆

YOUR STORY CHARACTER IS
Confident
Ambitious
Encouraging
Loyal

BUT ALSO
Bossy
Dramatic
Pompous
Boastful

☆ Capricorn ☆

YOUR STORY CHARACTER IS
Ambitious
Intelligent
Responsible
Trustworthy

BUT ALSO
Penny-pinching
Pessimistic
Overbearing
Mysterious

☆ Sagittarius ☆

YOUR STORY CHARACTER IS
Independent
Positive
Adventurous
Chatty

BUT ALSO
Unemotional
To the point
Disorganised
Easily bored

☆ Scorpio ☆

YOUR STORY CHARACTER IS
Inventive
Creative
Lively
Enthusiastic

BUT ALSO
Jealous
Stubborn
Sly
Obsessive

ALL ABOUT NICK

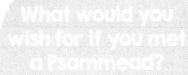

We had lots of burning questions for Nick! Here are his answers...

What would you pick to take with you on a desert island?

My own very comfy bed and an endless supply of beautifully laundered bed linen.

What would you wish for if you met a Psammead?

It would be nice to go back in time to my 20s and live that decade again, but this time with a bit more self-confidence.

What's your favourite snack when you're sketching?

Sweeties — ideally lemon sherberts.

What's your favourite season of the year? Why?

I like summer best. I just love it when I can feel the sun on my skin and it's warm enough to be barefoot all day long.

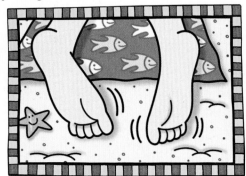

What do you think would happen if Tracy met Hetty?

I think, after sizing each other up, they'd get on very well.

94